STONER'S
OPTICAL ILLUSIONS

**OVER 100
MIND-BENDING
ILLUSIONS TO TRIP
YOUR MIND**

Published in 2021 by Welbeck
An imprint of Welbeck Non-Fiction Limited,
part of Welbeck Publishing Group,
20 Mortimer Street London W1T 3JW.

Text and Design © Welbeck Non-Fiction Limited,
part of Welbeck Publishing Group.

Design and Illustrations: Design to Print Solutions
Text: Jason Ward
Editorial: Chris Mitchell

A CIP catalogue record for this book is available from the British Library

ISBN 978 1 78739 583 1

Printed in Dubai

10 9 8 7 6 5 4 3 2 1

STONER'S
OPTICAL ILLUSIONS

**OVER 100
MIND-BENDING
ILLUSIONS TO TRIP
YOUR MIND**

JAZ CIGARETTE

WELBECK

CONTENTS

DAZED AND CONFUSED

REEFER MADNESS

CONTENTS

HALF BAKED

EASY RIDER

UP IN SMOKE

INTRODUCTION

I've seen things. Uncanny correlations. Mad, pure color. Oh, yes. For as long as I can remember, I've been able to pay attention to carpet patterns, rainbows glinting in gasoline, the way that *2001: A Space Odyssey and A Day In The Life* are structurally and conceptually identical...

People tell me it's because of the heroic quantities of weed I ingest, and I tell people that it's because I have an enhanced capacity to appreciate. You look, but I *see*, you see?

Wait, where was I? My name is Jaz Cigarette. Did I tell you that already? I get lost sometimes. It's so trippy, man. Did you ever hear about nominative determinism? The idea is that if your name is John Fielder, say, you end up playing first base for the Milwaukee Brewers. It's an actual thing; look it up. What I'm saying is that it's inevitable I'd end up writing a book of pot-themed optical illusions. Or selling cigarettes in a booth on a railway platform, I guess?

The images in this book are strange and beautiful and messed up, and they make your brain tingle through some obscene neural magic. Some of them are fun to just stare at for a little while—oh boy, some are fun to stare at for a long while—and others totally mess with your mind. But in a good way, I promise. Did I mention that this is a book of optical illusions? Kidding, kidding.

Anyway, as a drill sergeant in a war movie would say: smoke 'em if you got 'em...

Your pal,

JAZ CIGARETTE

DAZED AND CONFUSED

JAMAICAN DREAM ↓

It's all a big grind, man. But which big
grinder is the biggest big grind(er)?

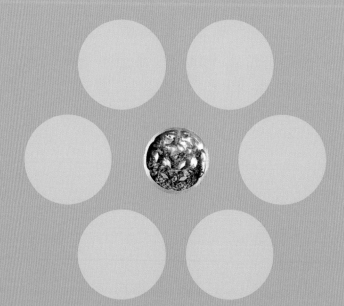

Answer see page 38

KALI MIST ↘

Hookah smoking is a great communal experience, but there's such a thing as too communal. How many people want to share your stuff?

Answer see page 38

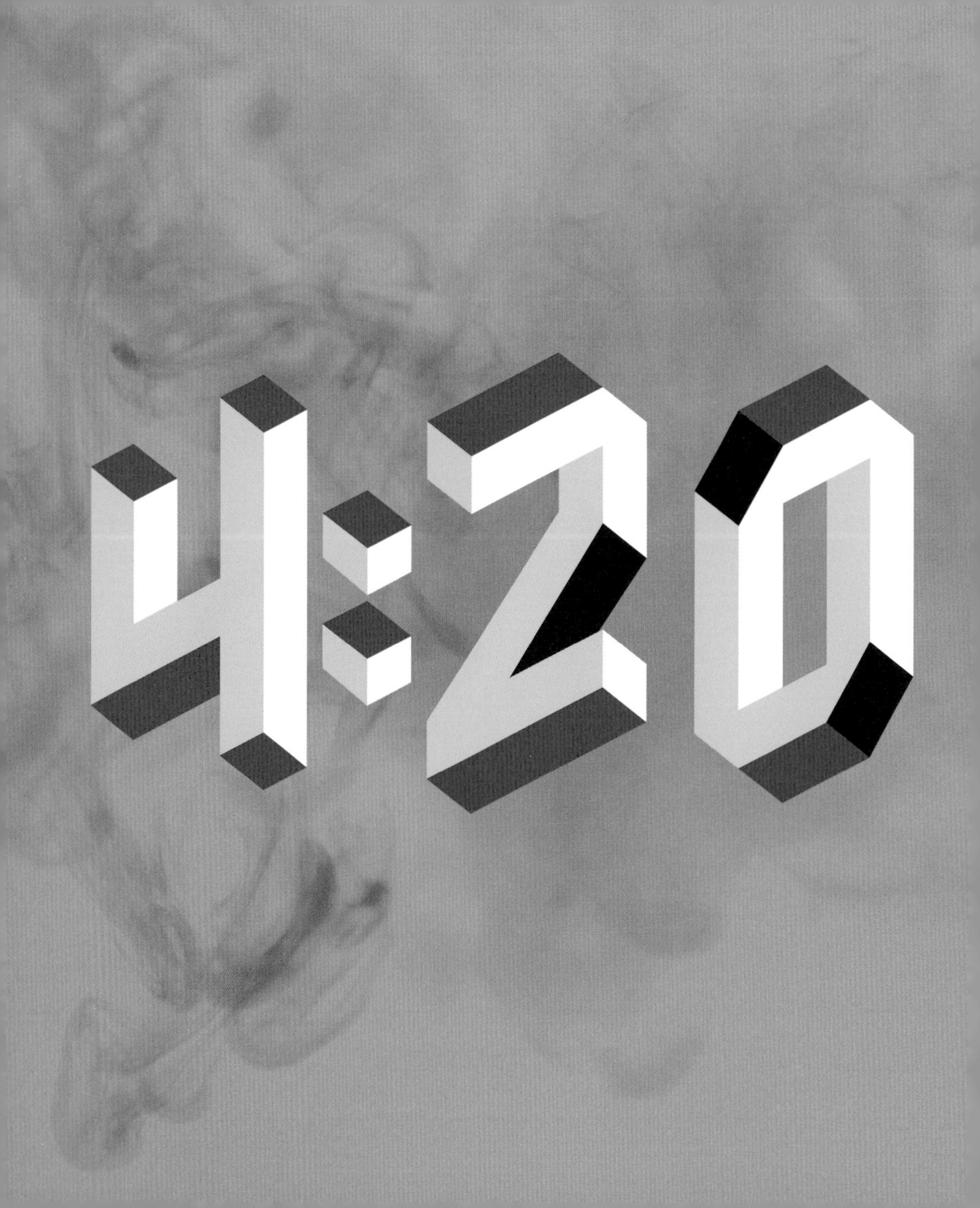
4:20

RED EYE ↓

There are laws humans have been known to break (in *physics*, dude)... and those you can't break because you'd violate Euclidean geometry. These matches would be cool if they weren't impossible. Maybe that makes them cooler?

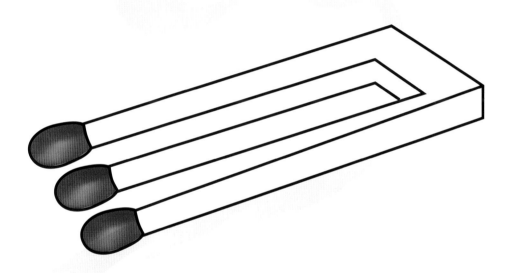

ヘ SWISS

DOUBLE TANGIE BANANA ↓

Oh hey, I've just remembered that this
is a book of optical illusions. Intense!
Are these spirals or circles?

APPLE SHERBET ↗

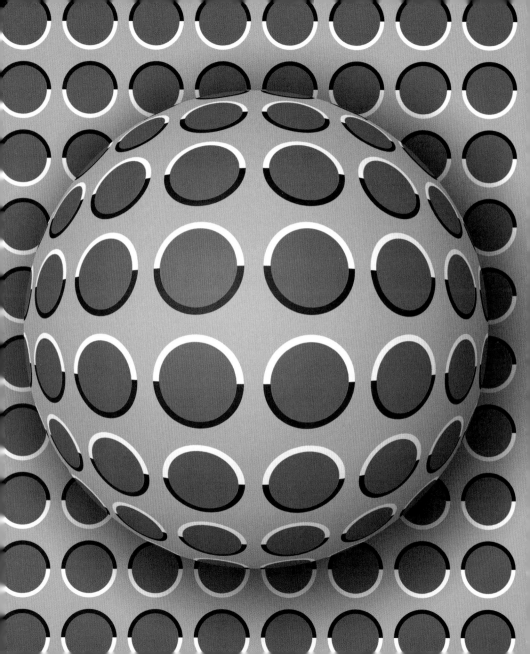

BELLADONNA ↓

David Bowie, is that you? He's back! Everything's
gonna be alright. Which pupil is the biggest?

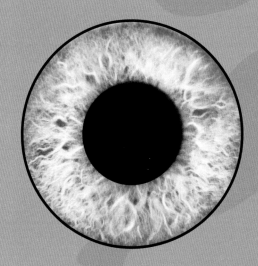
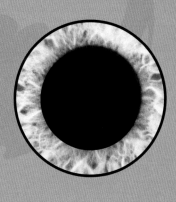

↖ NEVILLE'S HAZE

Answer see page 38

ALIEN RIFT ↓

It's well known that fish get longer
the more stoned they are. Swordfish are
permanently wasted, trust me. Which
of these fish is the most stoned?

↖ **LEMON G**

ZOMBIE KUSH ↓

Speaking of onions, I think an individual onion should be called a "one-nion." It'd save so much time. And what's up with these bendy squares? Seriously, I'm getting giddy over here.

↖ **PROFESSOR CHAOS**

Answer see page 39

THE BLOOD ↓

This vampire bat is hiding something—
probably its thirst for blood.

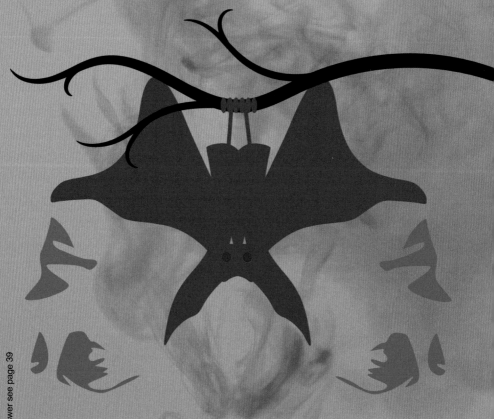

Answer see page 39

MALAWI ↗

SOUR POISON ↓

I'm not going to tell you how to live your
life, but apparently something weird
happens if you stare at this for a minute,
and then turn your gaze to a wall.

TORA BORA ↗

CHEMO ↓

They say this hookah is impossible to smoke. I've never been one to back away from a challenge, though.

SWISS TSUNAMI →

🍁
28

SHIVA SKUNK ↓

Sweet spiral. I might even run my finger around it, just to check.

↖ **SOUTH INDIAN**

COLOMBIAN GOLD ↓

Is it just me, or is the bong affecting these lines?
They've got magical properties, I swear.

MEXICAN ↗

Answer see page 39

WEDDING CAKE ↓

Did you know that The Rock used to eat 821 pounds of cod a year? That's way too much cod, man. I think he stopped because they were running out or something. Woah, is that wheel turning?

OG CHEM ↗

LEMON AMNESIA ↓

Now I fancy some cod, I don't know why.
Oh yeah, can you make this pulsing leaf
stay still by focusing on its center?

TULIP ↓

It looks like these bongs have been sent to prison. They should have said they were for ornamental use only. What colors are they?

Answer see page 39

ANSWERS

JAMAICAN DREAM

These circles are known as an Ebbinghaus illusion, or Titchener circles. The closer the surrounding circles are to the central circle, the larger it appears.

BELLADONNA

Neither pupil is bigger, they're both the same size. This is a Delboeuf illusion, caused by the same visual processes behind the Ebbinghaus illusion.

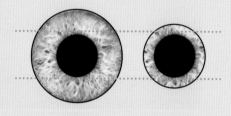

KALI MIST

There are six faces.

ALIEN RIFT

The fish are the same length and therefore equally stoned.

ZOMBIE KUSH

This checkerboard appears to bend due to the position of the black and white dots. Our brains interpret the margin between the dots and the borders as lines, skewing our perception.

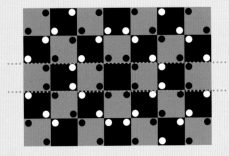

COLOMBIAN GOLD

While the green and orange lines appear aligned, it's actually the green and purple ones that are aligned. This happens because our perceptual systems tend to "expand" acute angles, perceiving them as larger angles than they really are.

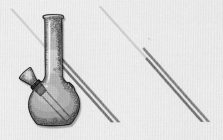

THE BLOOD

There are two faces hidden upside-down in the image.

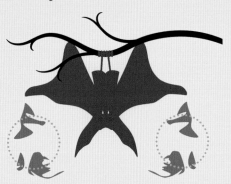

TULIP

Both bongs are actually the same color; the black and white lines trick the brain.

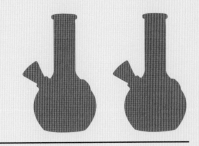

REEFER
MADNESS

ZKITTLEZ ↓

I don't know who's been rolling these joints, but they're definitely not the same length, right?

A

B

Answer see page 68

CHEMDAWG ↗

DARK STAR ↓

Please tell me that these dots keep disappearing and reappearing for you, too? How many are there, even?

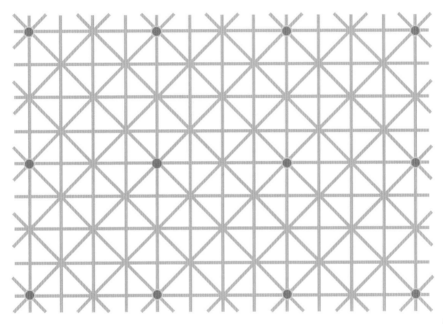

↖ CHEESE QUAKE

HEADWRECKER ↓

Joints, jays, phatties, it's all the same to me.
I just want to know which one is longer.

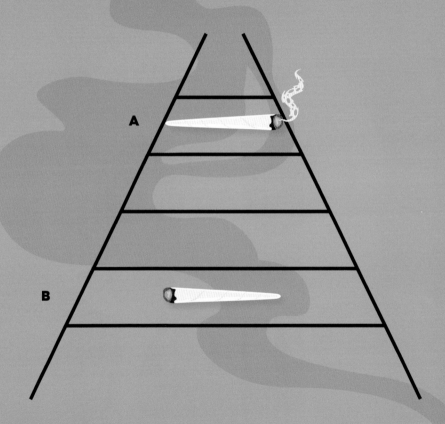

↖ **STRAWBERRY COUGH**

Answer see page 68

REEFER FUN ↓

Imagine if you entered your home one
day and saw this. I don't think you'd
ever come back from it.

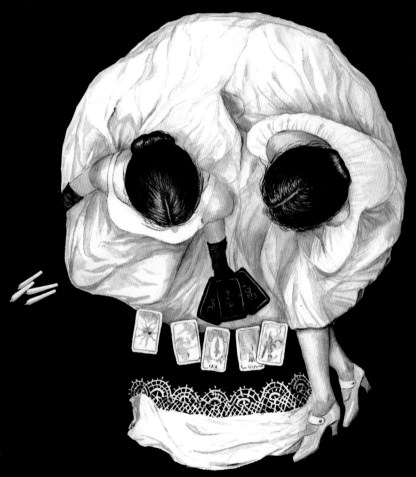

HAWAIIAN SNOW ↓

HAWAIIAN PUNCH ↓

I think these two are hiding
something, although it's definitely
not their grass. Amateurs!

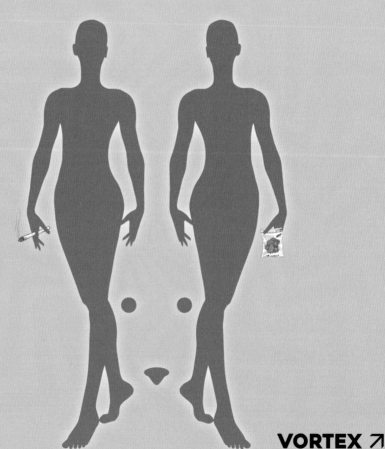

VORTEX ↗

NORTHERN LIGHTS ↓

To see what's within these trees, I'd recommend smoking some trees, if you know what I mean.

Answer see page 69

ALPHA BLUE ↗

↓ **BLACKBERRY DREAM**

↖ **BERRY BOMB**

DURBAN POISON ↓

I know which one I'd prefer to sit at.
Spoiler alert: it's the one with the weed
on it. Which table is bigger though?

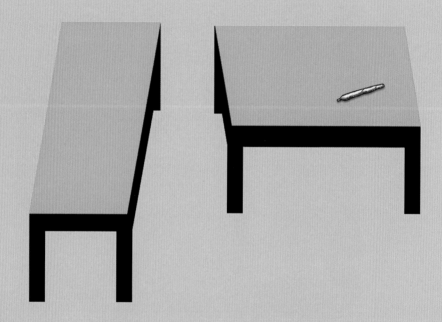

Answer see page 69

INCREDIBLE HULK ↗

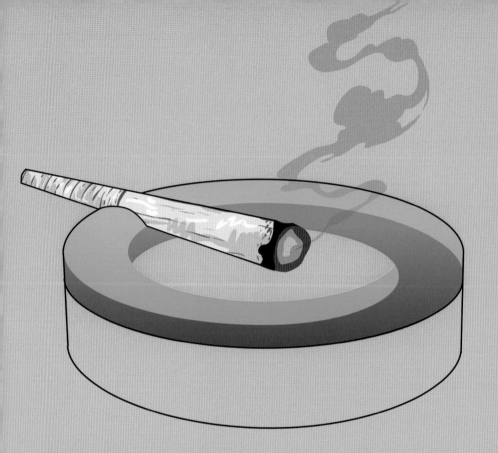

BLUE DREAM HAZE ↑

I don't want to say that this ashtray
is harshing my buzz, but it just doesn't
seem possible to me.

POWER PLANT ↓

I'm probably giving too much away,
but if you added a zero here you'd
get my second favorite number.

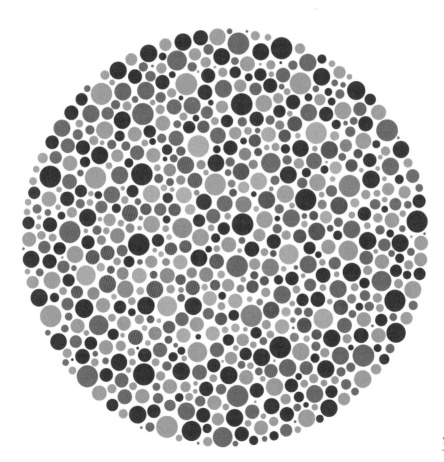

SILVER HAZE ↓

CAPTAIN CAKE ↓

Obviously, the objective here is to choose the longer reefer, right? A longer reefer means a longer smoke; that's just science.

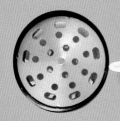

Answer see page 69

WHITE NIGHTMARE ↓

My friend Ralph showed me something cool. Hold two joints level in front of you, focus on them, and slowly bring the tips together. Easy, right? Now try it with one eye open. Unless you've got any better ideas for what to do with two joints?

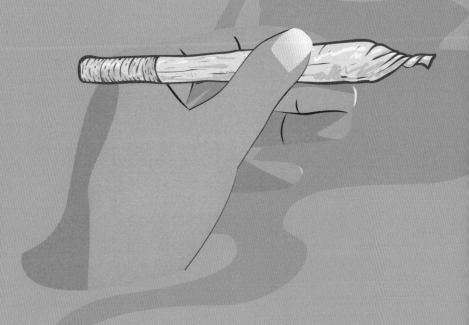

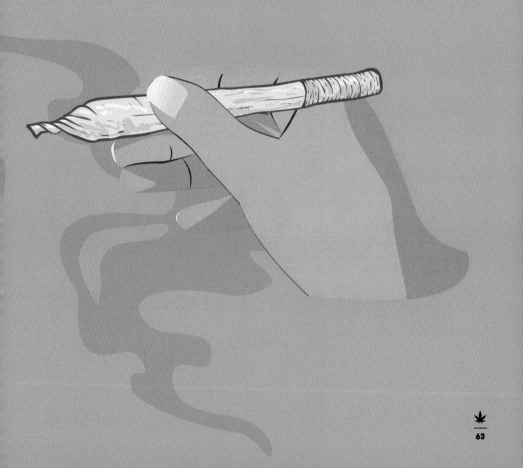

APPLE JACK ↓

I swear this apple core is talking
about me. Am I just hallucinating?

HURKLE ↗

VARIN ↓

So many marijuana leaves! I feel like I'm in a head shop. I'll just do what I usually do in such circumstances: focus on the central leaf and move my head forward until something cool happens.

THAI ↗

ANSWERS

ZKITTLEZ

The two spliffs are identical. There are competing theories for why the lower one appears to be larger – the common explanation is that the brain is confused by the difference in size between the large and the small radius. The short side makes the long side appear longer, and the long side makes the short side appear even shorter.

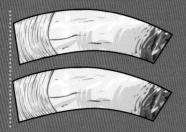

HEADWRECKER

Neither spliff is longer.
This is known as a Ponzo illusion.

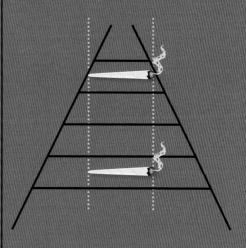

DARK STAR

There are 12 dots, but most people are unable to see them all concurrently, as the brain fills in the mental image on the periphery of their focus.

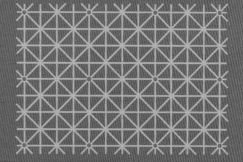

HAWAIIAN PUNCH

A rabbit is hidden between
the two figures.

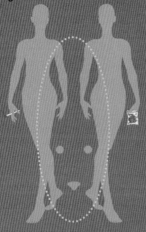

DURBAN POISON

The tables are actually the same size, but our eyes
miscalculate their lengths when we decode them
according to rules for three-dimensional objects.

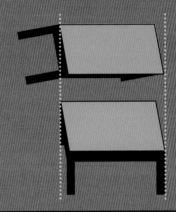

NORTHERN LIGHTS

The tree branches form the shape
of a woman's head.

CAPTAIN CAKE

Both joints are the same size, and so will give an
equally long smoke.

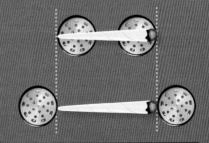

HALF
BAKED

LEMON POUND CAKE ↓

This is what it must be like to hang out with Snoop Dogg. Maybe he can tell me if the joints are longer on the left or right side.

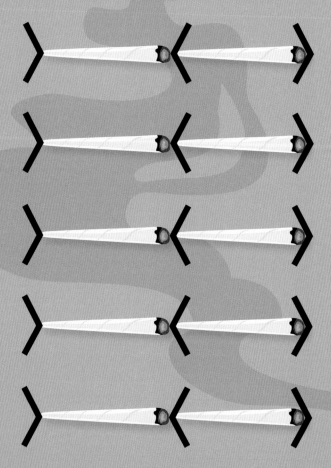

Answer see page 98

NEPALESE ↓

I wouldn't recommend touching the
shells of real snails—be kind, dude—but
are you steady enough to trace this spiral?

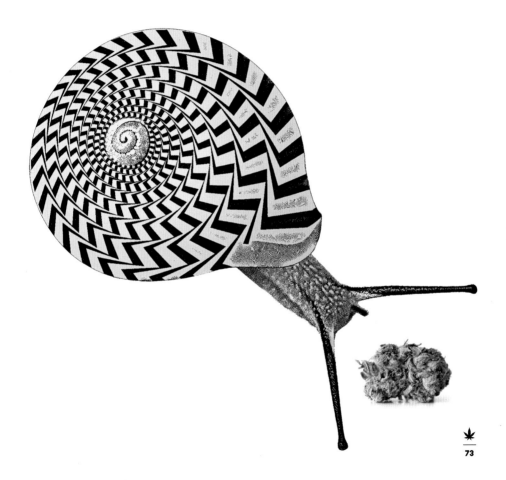

KILIMANJARO ↓

Look at this guy; I think he's a little
stoned! If those blocks are uneven
then he's in real trouble.

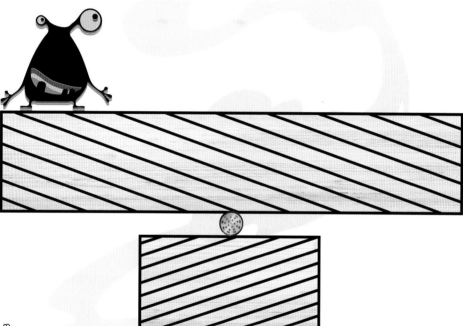

STRAWBERRY ↗

CHERRY LIME HAZE ↓

I don't know how I ended up in this 1980s maze with a couple of Buddhas. I don't even know which one is bigger.

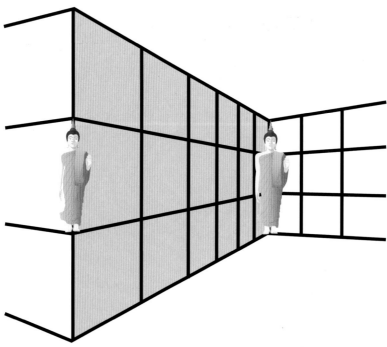

CINDERELLA'S DREAM ↗

Oh, this one is clever, this is. Try squinting at this elegant lady and watch her transform. Freaky. Hint: is it a necklace or a mouth?

PINEAPPLE OG ↓

This is some straight-up Dalí shit.
That butterfly is... melting?
Unless something else is going on?

Answer see page 98

ISLAND SWEET SKUNK ↗

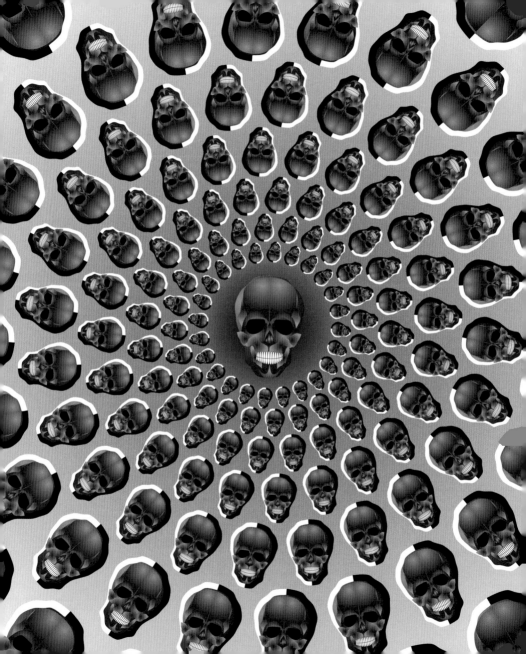

CHEM CRUSH ↓

Do you want to hear my theory about how John Lennon
would still be alive if the B-52's hadn't recorded "Rock Lobster"?
Oh, okay then. Well, then tell me if these leaves are different colors.

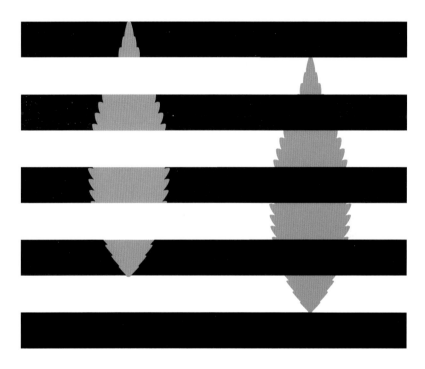

↖ PURPLE URKLE

SUNDAE DRIVER ↓

By the way, the B-52's were as innovative as Talking Heads, but they knew how to fucking party. Anyway, I need to stop smoking, because I can't tell if these lines are straight.

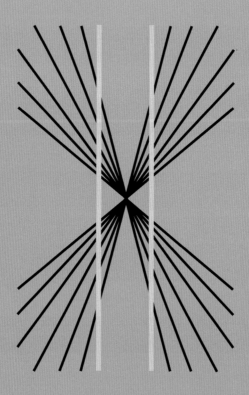

Answer see page 99

SOUR COOKIES ↗

GHOST TRAIN HAZE ↓

There's no way that life isn't a simulation. I just tried focusing on the Buddha and moving my head toward and away from the page, and now I'm getting serious déjà vu. This has to be the Matrix.

DONEGAL ↗

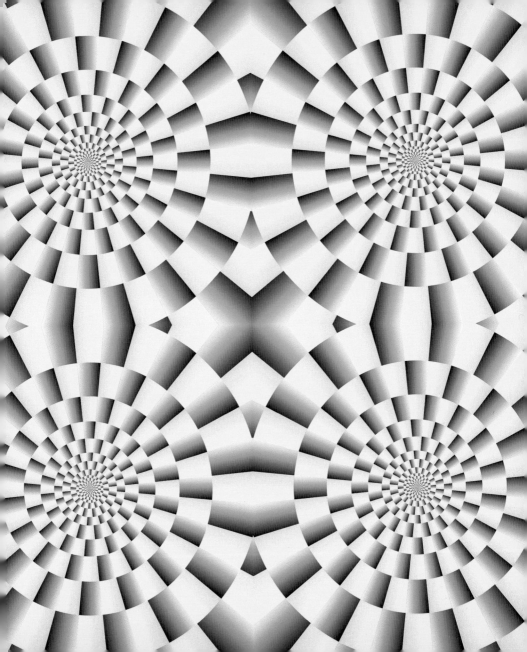

ROMULAN GRAPEFRUIT ↓

Trying to get my hookah on these
stairs will make me literally trippy, LOL.

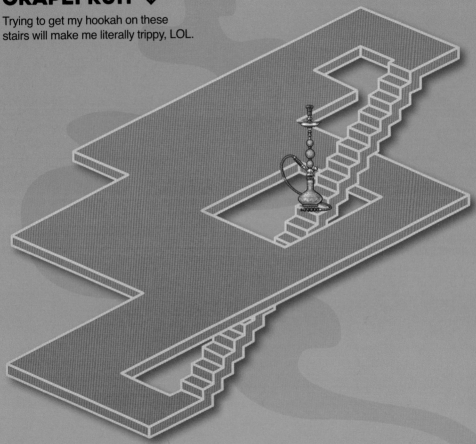

↖ **PURPLE STAR**

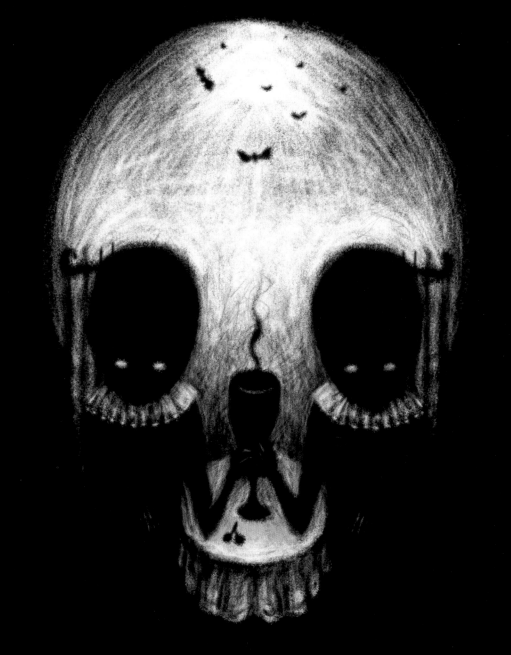

NIGHT TERROR ↓

Watch out for this creepy thing! I'm not even going to look at those messed-up twins on the other page, otherwise I'll wake up in a bathtub filled with ice.

↖ **FULL MOON**

KING'S BREAD ↓

Which box of canned cannabis is bigger?
Wait, does cannabis come in cans?
Why would it be canned if it's in a box?
I demand logic!

↖ FORBIDDEN FRUIT

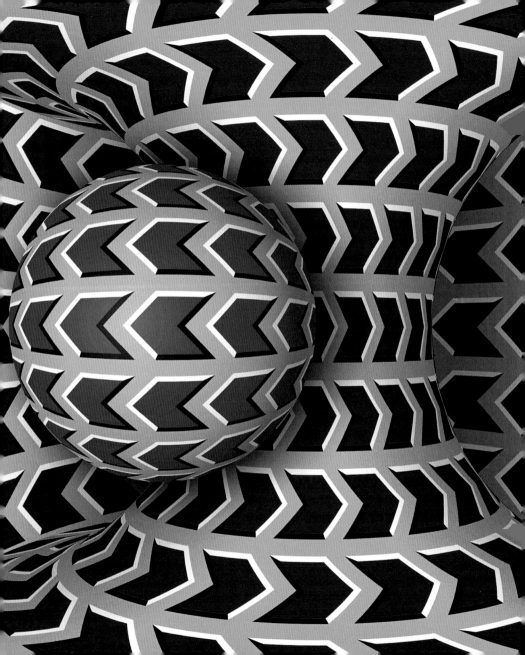

DOUBLE DREAM ↓

This tree looks gnarly—get it?

↖ **WHITE 99**

MOONBOW ↓

I've seen bongs that are absolute
works of art, but I can't work out
what's so different about these two.

AK-48 ↗

ICE CREAM CAKE ↓

Quack, quack or... wait, what sound
does a rabbit make? Like a pffft pffft?
Hold on, I'm gonna google it. Okay.
It's like a squeaky purr. What were
we talking about?

Answer see page 99

CATFISH ↗

ANSWERS

LEMON POUND CAKE

The left and right joints are the same length. This is known as the Müller-Lyer illusion; the explanation for this phenomena has been debated since its creation in 1889.

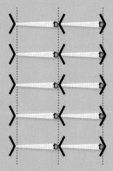

KILIMANJARO

The blocks are both level—the diagonal lines and placing of the creature trick the mind into seeing the top block as uneven.

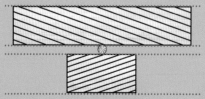

CHERRY LIME HAZE

In this variation on the Ponzo illusion, both Buddhas are the same size.

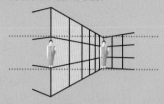

PINEAPPLE OG

There are two downward-looking heads hiding in the butterfly's wings.

CHEM CRUSH

The leaves are both the same color but look different due to the black and white lines. This is called the Bezold effect.

SUNDAE DRIVER

The lines are straight. This is known as the Herring illusion. When two straight, parallel lines are in front of a radial background, they appear as if they were bowed outward.

KING'S BREAD

Both boxes are the same size. Named after Stanford psychologist Roger N. Shepard, this is called a Shepard table illusion.

DOUBLE DREAM

There are two faces in the trunk.

MOONBOW

There's actually no difference between the bongs. Our perception of color is influenced by what surrounds it, so our brains register the bongs as different colors due to the gradient behind them.

ICE CREAM CAKE

It's a duck and a rabbit. The ambiguous image induces multi-stable perception, where it's possible for a single image to provide different, unchanging perceptions.

EASY
RIDER

GLASS APPLE ↑

I totally forgot what I was looking
at here, which is ironic, because...
I can't remember why.

ALPINE BLUE ↗

GOLDEN TICKET ↓

Oof. OOF. I need to get my head straight; it's as wonky as these bars. Are these bars wonky? Who am I talking to? Hello?

Answer see page 128

KING LOUIS ↗

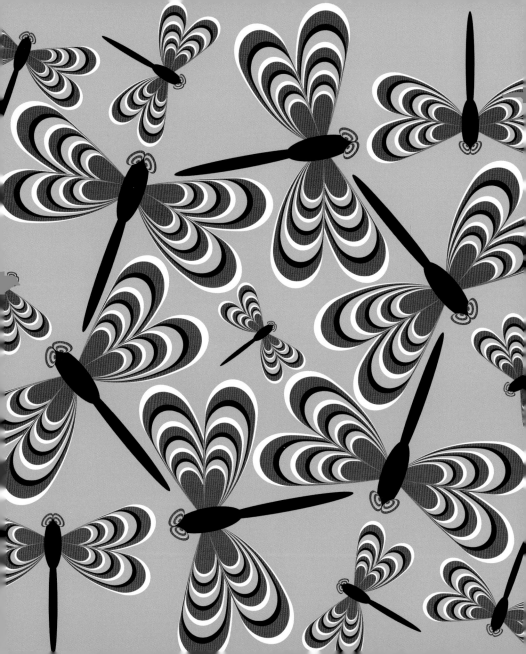

LEMON JACK ↓

↖ INDIAN SWEET SKUNK

SLURRICANE ↓

Did you hear about that Buddha statue in
Thailand that spent 200 years covered in
stucco and no one knew that it was actually
made of gold underneath? That was wild.
Imagine if your toaster was gold and you
had no idea.

MIDNIGHT ↗

HEADBAND ↓

For real, it'd be cool if my neighbor's cat smoked weed. He needs to chill out.

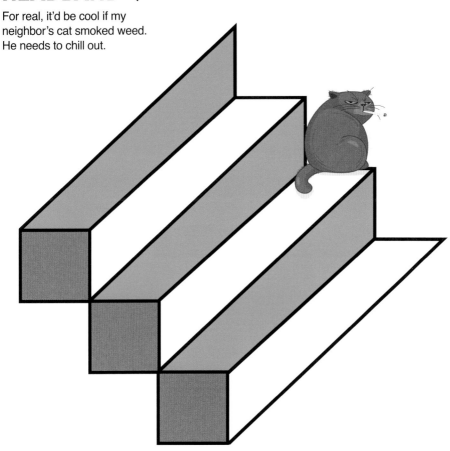

↖ **DOMINATOR**

HARLEQUIN ↓

Buddhas on a train track! They'd better watch out.
Which is the biggha Buddha, buddy?

Answer see page 128

CRITICAL MASS ↗

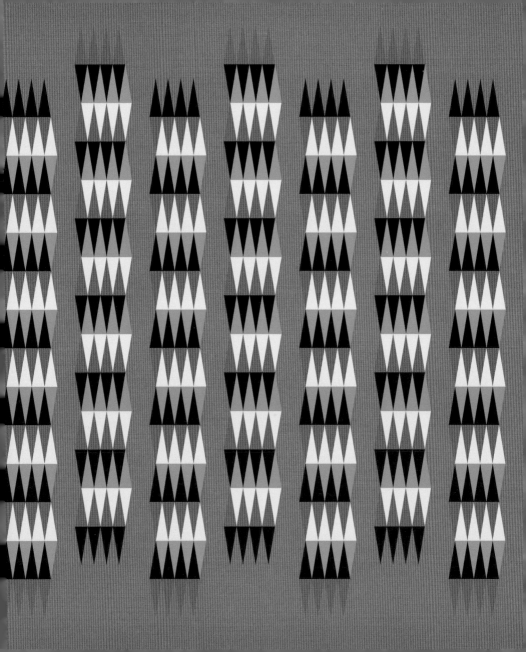

ROYAL HIGHNESS ↓

Did you know that if you watch the *Wizard of Oz* while listening to *Dark Side of the Moon* this image will still make no sense?

↖ **ASIAN FANTASY**

REDHEADED STRANGER ↓

Apparently this concept first appeared
in a German humor magazine in 1892.
I bet the German humor magazines in
1892 were absolutely hilarious.

↖ SKUNK HERO

Answer see page 129

SOUR CHOCOLATE ↓

Be cool, just be cool... let's pretend like there isn't a massive eye staring at us from the other page. Um, so, what happens when you look directly at one of these dots?

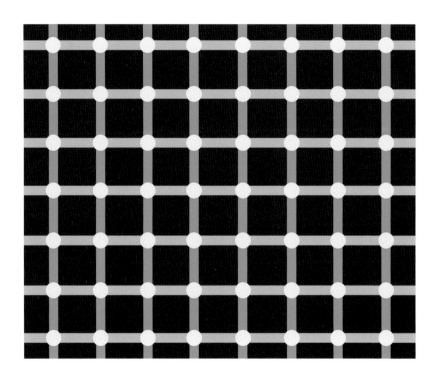

WILD THAILAND ↗

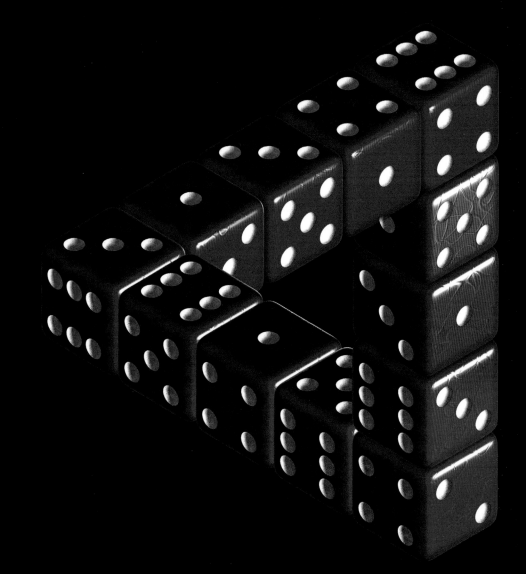

SOUR HAZE ↓

My buddy Ralph—do you know Ralph?
Ralph is the coolest; you gotta meet him.
Ralph says these bongs are the same
color, but he won't tell me what color
it is. Fuck Ralph.

↖ JILLYBEAN

Answer see page 129

GREEN CRACK ↓

Did I tell you about my boy Ralph? Okay, well, Ralph also says these leaves are all the same color. I don't know why Ralph is so obsessed with colors these days; it's a real problem.

SUPER GREEN CRACK ↗

WHITE DIESEL ↓

Check out this Goldilocks shit right here. I'll take
the biggest one—right on!

Answer see page 129

WILLIE NELSON ↗

DUTCH TREAT ↓

If I had a joint right now, it wouldn't
be lying on an impossible object,
I'll tell you that much.

JACK THE CLEANER ↗

ANSWERS

GLASS APPLE

The branches look like
an elephant.

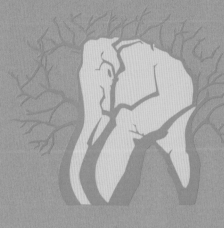

HARLEQUIN

They are actually the same size. It is another
Ponzo illusion.

GOLDEN TICKET

The bars are straight, but the black and
white diamonds in the junctions make them
look as if they slant. This is now known as a
café wall illusion, after the tiles of a café wall
in Bristol, England.

REDHEADED STRANGER

It's both a rabbit and a duck. 60 years after its first appearance, the rabbit-duck was made famous by the philosopher Ludwig Wittgenstein.

SOUR HAZE

The bongs are both red, but the blue and yellow lines trick the eye.

SOUR CHOCOLATE

This is a scintillating grid illusion where dots seem to appear and disappear at the intersections of two lines crossing each other. It's believed that this comes from a neural process called lateral inhibition, where an excited neuron reduces the activity of its neighbors.

WHITE DIESEL

Sorry, mate, but the hookahs are all the same size. Need a bit of Goldilocks' cake instead, I think.

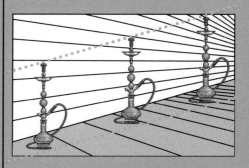

UP IN SMOKE

BLACKWATER ↓

Fun fact: I once consumed an edible and watched the *Lego Movie* and became obsessed with how they'd added thumbprints onto the bricks. Anyway, the big one at the top looks pretty sweet, right?

↖ **BIG SMOOTH**

Answer see page 158

QUERKLE ↓

Fucked-up Rubik's cube says what!

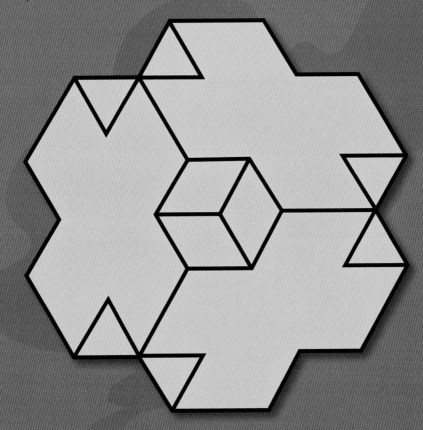

↖ **CHRONIC THUNDER**

🌿
135

RAINMAKER ↓

This would totally be the last thing you'd
see if you got eaten by a dice alien.

BLUE MAGOO ↗

MR. NICE GUY ↓

Not to brag, but I bet this is that Möbius guy's favorite book. Or is he dead? Time is so fickle, man.

↖ **SHIVA SKUNK**

ROMULAN ↓

Have you ever noticed how marijuana
leaves look just like the Adidas symbol?
That can't be a coincidence, surely?
Anyway, what color are these?

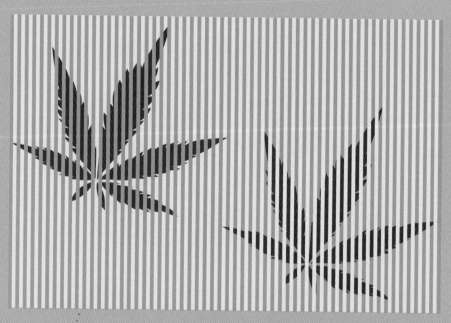

Answer see page 158

BLACK MAMBA ↗

CADILLAC PURPLE ↓

I'm supposed to ask if these boxes are all the same size, but do you know what I can't stop thinking about? In the song "Miami," Will Smith says "ain't no surprise in the club to see Sly Stallone." IMAGINE SEEING SYLVESTER STALLONE IN A NIGHTCLUB.

Answer see page 158

PURPLE PASSION ↗

AMERICAN PIE ↓

Squares or spirals? Let's keep moving
because that image on the left is *throbbing*.
I need to lie down; I'm not kidding.

↖ **BRAZILIAN**

BANANA
SPLIT ↓

Here's a little weed-smoking strategy, free of charge: always smoke the longer one. Also: "Wellness" is late capitalism's attempt to profit off the anxiety caused by late capitalism.

Answer see page 158

FROSTY ↗

OREGON LEMONS ↓

This would make a good logo for a
Swedish death metal band with a name
like Gölgötha or Långfjäll or something.

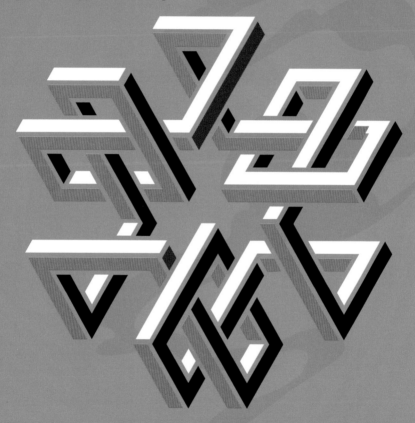

DAWG'S WALTZ ↗

GOBBILYGOO ↓

I know I should be used to it by now, but it's so messed up how the shelf becomes inverted halfway through. What are these people on, seriously?

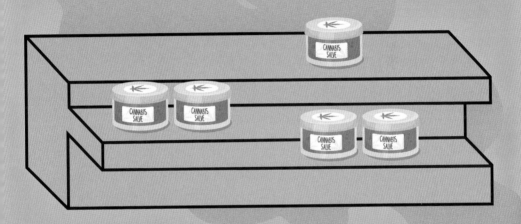

↖ SILVERBACK GORILLA

DIABLO ↓

Oh, I get it! There are words in here. Neat.

STAR KILLER ↗

PACIFIC BLUE ↓

Maybe this is how they make dice?
What's inside a die, anyway? Is it just
more plastic? You'd be able to tell if
they were hollow, surely?

↖ DONKEY BUTTER

NUKEN ↓

I feel like I'm in the movie *Inception* right now. You have to tell me if you're trying to incept me, otherwise it's entrapment. No, wait, that doesn't sound right. Never mind, I'm off for a lie down and a smoke. Peace.

↖ **DUCT TAPE**

ANSWERS

BLACKWATER

The "big one" is actually the same size as the others.

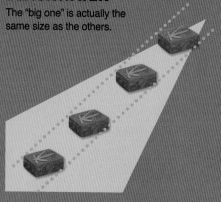

CADILLAC PURPLE

The boxes are all the same size but some of them have white borders, which makes them appear to be smaller.

ROMULAN

The leaves are both the same shade of red, even though one appears darker.

BANANA SPLIT

While smoking the longer joint is a good strategy, these two are both the same length.

DIABLO

The hidden words are LOOK and LOVE.

CREDITS

The publishers would like to thank the following sources for their kind permission to reproduce the pictures in this book.

Getty Images: Universal History Archive/Universal Images Group 116

Blaine20 via Creative Commons Atttribution-Share Alike 4.0 International licence: 23

Public Domain: 12, 59, 66, 76, 77, 82, 84, 103, 104, 145

© Gianni A. Sarcone, giannisarcone.com: 21, 73

Shutterstock: Argus 143; /Arkela 51, 80; /Artoptimum 14 (background); /Aataish Bhatia 72; /Art of Sun 141; / Atomic Roderick 57; /Barry Barnes 34; /Olga Beliaeva 48; /Betacam-SP 126, 148; /BigAlbalBaloo 31; /Zhitkob Boris 28t, 32; /Branding Pot 104; /Burlak 137; /Clenpies Design 108; /CYAM 73; /DesignR: 84; /DiskoVisnja 122; /Elenasz 60; /Excentro 157; /Foxyimage 100; / Frank_kle 22; /Peter Hermes Furian 136, 155; /J Gade 107; /Gomolach 15; /GrAl 24, 50, 78; /Mark Grenier 20. 30,43 53, 54, 122, 65, 109, 114, 119, 123, 127, 132, 156; /Grimgram 41, 130; /Guntum_crr 81; /HappyPictures 16, 94, 133, 150; /Hunky 21, 50, 117; /Idea Trader 10, 18, 46, 47; /Incredible_movements 74; /INelson 70; / Iotan 85, 97, 103, 138; /Jastrow illusion: 42t; /JYGraphic 63; /Barandash Karandashich 88; /Katyau 31t; /Nikita Konashenkov 42, 58, 62; /Andrey Korshenkov 33, 95, 105, 144; /Labelvector 102; /Lulias 106; /MoreVector 32, 37, 56; /Jacques Ninio 45; /Nofretka 110, 113; / Ol41ka 79; /Paseven 91; /Passion Artist 14; /Pavlo S 64; /Perepadia Y 17, 25, 86, 90, 92, 150, 154; /Pikepicture 29; /Pamamia 45; /Pixaroma 125; /Pravokruguinik 24; / Pretty Vectors 40b, 131; /S.Ragets 142; /Fouas A. Saad 107; /Sabelskaya 13, 28b; /Serglew 12; /Georgy Shafeev 27; /Skaska1980 64; /Anna Shestopalova 52; /Shooarts 115, 139; /Sirtravelalot 19; /Nikolay Solidcreature 152; / Svg Art Stock 112;/Sunset Suesakunkrit 93; /Takaip 76, 108; /Skripnichenko Tatiana 55; /Jethroe Toe 111; / Titus Group 74; /Tony4urban 117; /Troyka 26, 149; / Tynyuk 13; /Dmytro Tyschchenko 61; /Anci Valiart 135; / Cath Vectorielle 89;/VectoriX 120; /Vectroyer 35; /Andrei Verner 47, 58, 61, 138, 146; /Lena Vetka 104; /Iva Villi WinWin Artlab 15, 23; /Vitaliken 87, 135, 151; /Andrey Korshenkov 153

Welbeck Publishing: 37, 49, 67, 75, 83, 96, 104, 118, 121, 124, 140, 144

Every effort has been made to acknowledge correctly and contact the source and/or copyright holder of each picture and Welbeck Publishing apologises for any unintentional errors or omissions, which will be corrected in future editions of this book.